MORE TALES OF
GODS AND DEMONS FROM

INDIAN MYTHOLOGY

MORE TALES OF GODS & DEMONS FROM

INDIAN MYTHOLOGY

CONTENTS

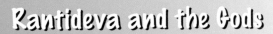

URVASHI AND PURURAVAS

Once, Lord Indra was perturbed by the deep meditation of two powerful sages, Nara and Narayana. So, he created a beautiful nymph and sent her to break the concentration of the sages. The sages got angry at this and called Indra there.

Urvashi and Pururavas

"What you have done is unethical, Indra!" Nara shouted. "And don't be proud that only you can create a nymph!" Narayana said. Then he slapped his thigh and out came a nymph. "She is urvashi!" said the sage. Indra had never seen such beauty.

"As a penalty, you'll have to look after her!" said Nara. Indra realised his mistake and accepted the punishment. Urvashi soon became popular in the heavens. But she had fallen in love with Indra's friend, King Pururavas, who stayed on earth.

One day, a sage cursed Urvashi that she be thrown out of the heaven and live on earth. Urvashi was happy in her heart as she would now be able to meet her beloved. As soon as she was transferred to earth, she went to Pururavas's palace.

The king saw Urvashi and fell in love with her. "Marry me, dear!" he said. "On some conditions!" said Urvashi, "That my two pet lambs should never be harmed, and that I must never see you disrobed." The king agreed and they were married.

Meanwhile, there was unrest in the heavens. Indra was worried at Urvashi's sudden disappearance. He sent two Gandharvas on earth to find out Urvashi. The Gandharvas were the heavenly musicians who had magical powers.

Now it so happened that the Gandharvas spotted Urvashi in Pururavas's palace. By their powers, they also came to know about Urvashi's conditions for marriage. They knew that Urvashi wouldn't come with them willingly. So, they made a plan.

That night, the Gandharvas secretly entered into the palace and stole away Urvashi's lambs. When Urvashi heard the lambs bleating, she woke up with a start. "Help! My lambs!" Urvashi screamed of fear and shock.

Seeing Urvashi's hysterical behaviour, Pururavas couldn't hold back. He sprang out of his bed and went after the thieves. But he forgot to put on his robes. And Urvashi saw him disrobed!
The plan of the Gandharvas had worked out well.

When Pururavas realised his mistake, he instantly returned to his chamber. "You have broken the condition! I'll have to leave!" said Urvashi, sobbing. "B...but I didn't do it deliberately!" said Pururavas. But Urvashi left him weeping.

Pururavas couldn't live without Urvashi.
So, he began to pray to Lord Vishnu.
After many years of penance, Pururavas
was able to appease Vishnu, who in turn
blessed him to be reunited with Urvashi.
And then they lived happily ever after.

Bhima Slays Vakasura

BHIMA SLAYS VAKASURA

In the Mahabharata, Bhima was one
of the five Pandavas, who were an
eyesore to their cousins, the Kauravas.
Duryodhana, the Kaurava prince, once
made a wicked plan and forced his blind
father to send the Pandavas and their
mother on a holiday.

The Pandavas had suspicion but they kept quiet. The next day, they, along with their mother Kunti, left for Varnavarta, a place in the forest. There, Duryodhana had kept a palace ready for them. The Pandavas were surprised. They settled in the palace.

The unique fact about the palace was that it had been built completely with wood and hay. The Pandavas discussed among themselves and began to dig up a secret tunnel in the palace, so that they could escape if anything untoward happened.

One night, Duryodhana's men set the wooden palace on fire. Duryodhana was happy. Soon, the news spread that the Pandavas died in an accidental fire. But no one knew that actually they had escaped safely through the tunnel.

The Pandavas came to the other end of the forest. They took off their royal robes and dressed up in clothes made of bark-fibre. "Let the people think we are dead," thought Bhima. "I shall wait for the right time to avenge upon Duryodhana!"

As, the five brothers and Mother Kunti wandered in the forest, they came upon a Brahmin's hut. "Who are you all?" asked the Brahmins. "We are ascetics!" replied the Pandavas. "Can we stay here for some days?" "Why not?" said the Brahmin.

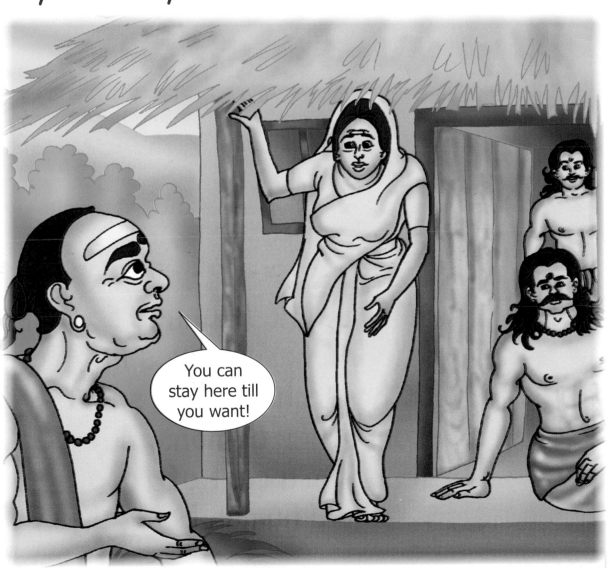

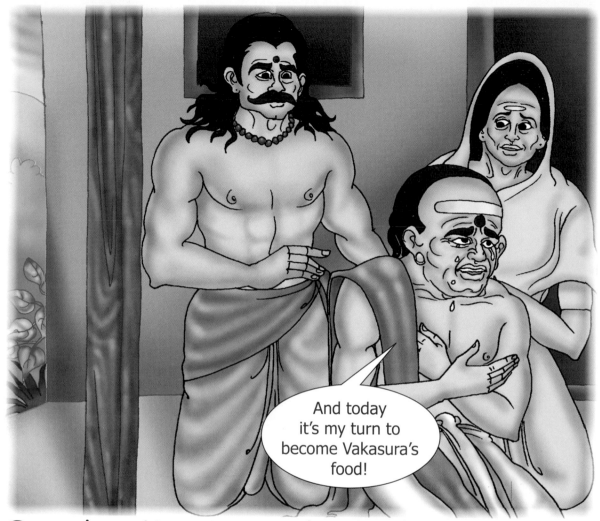

One day, Kunti saw the Brahmin crying. "A demon named Vakasura lives in this forest," said the Brahmin. "He saves our village from other demons, but we have to send him a cart of food, two buffaloes and a human being every day as food."

Kunti asked the Brahmin to send Bhima as the demon's food that day. At first, the Brahmin didn't agree. "Don't worry! my son will return safe!" said Kunti. So, that day, Bhima led the two buffaloes and the cart of food to Vakasura.

"No, you can't eat my food!" yelled the demon. "I will!" said Bhima. At this, Vakasura became furious. "How dare you?" he roared, charging at Bhima. A fierce duel ensued. Vakasura uprooted a tree and hurled it at Bhima.

Bhima was no less. He uprooted another tree and threw it at Vakasura. In no time, Bhima had overpowered the demon. With a jerk he broke Vakasura's spine and killed him. Then he loaded him on the cart and drove back to the village.

Seeing this, the Brahmin doubted that the people living in his hut were no ordinary men. Kunti then revealed the secret and requested him not to share it with anyone. The Brahmin felt grateful to the Pandavas and never revealed their secret.

Shiva and Ravana

SHIVA AND RAVANA

Ravana, the demon king of Lanka, was in distress when his mother, a devotee of Lord Shiva, came crying to him one day. "O son! I have lost the Lingam that I have been worshipping for so long," she said. "I won't take food till I get back the Lingam!"

Ravana promised his mother that he would go to Lord Shiva's abode asking for a Lingam. "I will do anything to get it for you, Mother!" said Ravana, "But please don't give up food!" Then Ravana started for Mount Kailash, Shiva's abode.

Reaching Mount Kailash, Ravana began his penance. He kindled five small fires and arranged them in a circle. At the centre of the circle, he stood upside down, on his head, and began to meditate. For thousands of years, Ravana prayed thus.

At the peak of his penance, Ravana was about to severe his head and offer it to Shiva. But before that Shiva appeared. "I am pleased, Ravana! Ask what you may!" he said. Ravana instantly said, "I want my three wishes to be fulfilled, O Lord!"

"As the first wish, make me immortal!"
said Ravana, "Secondly, give me a Lingam
that I shall carry home to my mother."
"So be it!" said Shiva. But he imposed
some conditions. "If you try to harm me,
you'll lose your first boon!" he said.

Ravana agreed to his conditions, then said, "As the third wish, give me a wife, as beautiful as your wife Uma!" "Now that is little difficult," said Shiva, "Because Uma is unparalleled in beauty." "Then give me Uma herself!" said Ravana.

Now Shiva was in a fix. He had promised to grant three wishes to Ravana. So, he had to part with Uma. Carrying Uma and the Lingam, and getting the boon of immortality, Ravana started back home. On his way, he met Sage Narada.

Narada's words bred suspicion in Ravana's mind and he went to Kailash. Shiva was sitting in meditation. In a fit of rage, Ravana forgot Shiva's condition and picked up a stone to hit him. Then and there, he lost the boon of immortality.

Ravana realised his mistake too late! Left with Uma and the Lingam, he carried them carefully. A passerby asked, "Why do you carry an old woman?" Ravana turned his head and looked at Uma. But he found an ugly old woman sitting on his shoulder.

Actually, Uma had cleverly transformed into an old woman. After chasing her away, Ravana was left with the Lingam. Suddenly, he felt the nature's call. "I must not keep it on the ground," he thought. So, he handed it over to a small boy.

But the Lingam was too heavy for the boy to hold. When Ravana returned, he saw the Lingam kept on the ground. Ravana caught hold of it and tried to lift it up. But the Lingam sank into the ground and all that Ravana could hold was a cow's ears.

The Curse of Bidhata

THE CURSE OF BIDHATA

There once lived a Brahmin with his wife in a small village. He was cursed by Bidhata, the God of Fate, that he would never be able to eat food to his full. So, the Brahmin would always lament for more food. And his wife would wonder what to do.

One day, the Brahmin got an invitation for a meal at the king's palace. So, he got up very early and reached the palace. "Welcome, O Brahmin!" said the king, and offered a seat to the Brahmin. Seeing the delicious dishes, the Brahmin was excited.

"Today, I shall definitely eat to my heart's content!" thought the Brahmin. But as soon as he took his first bite, a pot hanging overhead fell upon his plate and spoiled the food. "What's this?" the angry Brahmin yelled at the servants.

Hearing the Brahmin shout at the servants, the king came running in. "What happened, O Brahmin?" he asked. "The food is spoiled!" the Brahmin frowned his face. The king instantly ordered the cook to bring fresh food in clean plates.

The Brahmin began to eat. When Bidhata noticed him, he thought, "The Brahmin shouldn't enjoy a full meal!" So, he took the form of a golden frog and jumped into the Brahmin's food. Unaware of it, the Brahmin gulped the frog down his throat.

Bidhata was locked inside the Brahmin's belly. That day, the Brahmin happily ate up to his full. While on his way back home, he heard Bidhata calling for help from inside his belly. "Good!" said the Brahmin. "Be there! You have troubled me a lot!"

Now, there was a chaos in the heaven.
"We have to free Bidhata!" said the gods.
So, they went to Lord Vishnu and asked
for help. Vishnu asked Lakshmi, the
Goddess of Wealth and Luck, to go and
convince the Brahmin to release Bidhata.

Lakshmi instantly went to the Brahmin and asked him to let Bidhata out of his belly. The Brahmin shouted, "Why should I listen to you? You never bless a poor man like me!" Then he asked his wife to bring a broom and chased Lakshmi away.

Next, Vishnu sent Saraswati, the Goddess of Knowledge to the Brahmin. As soon as the Brahmin saw Saraswati, he shouted, "You won't receive any favours from me, for you didn't favour me while I was learning!" Then he chased her away, too.

At last, Lord Shiva intervened into the matter. Being his ardent devotee, the Brahmin calmly told him how Bidhata had tortured him. "Don't worry! You will get a place in my abode!" Shiva assured. The Brahmin then released Bidhata.

From that day, things widely changed for the Brahmin. He was no more a poor man. He could enjoy his food and get satisfied after eating. After living a happy life with his wife, the Brahmin died. As promised, Lord Shiva gave him a place in Kailash.

Krishna and Rukmini

KRISHNA AND RUKMINI

Rukmini was the daughter of King Bhishmaka of Vidarbha. She was stunningly beautiful. Right from her childhood, Rukmini happened to love Krishna, who lived in Dwarka. She thought about Krishna all the time.

Rukmini's brother Rukmi hated Krishna. He was aware of Rukmini's love for Krishna and so wanted to marry her elsewhere. One day, Rukmini came to know that Rukmi had fixed her marriage with Sisupala, the king of Chedi.

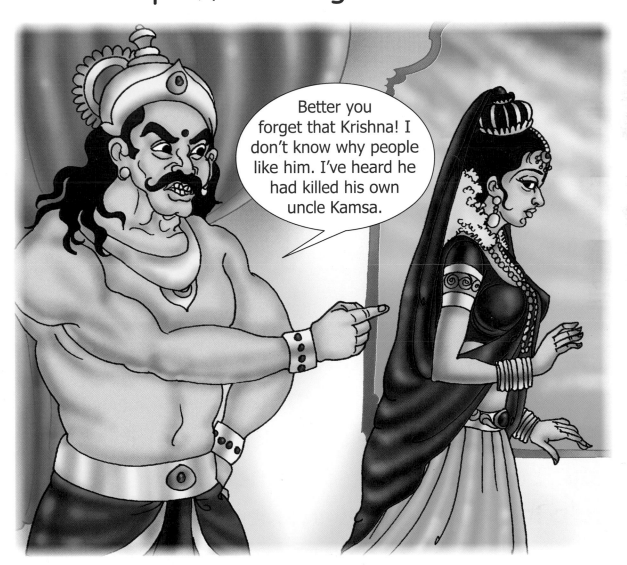

Getting worried, Rukmini wrote a letter to her beloved, informing him about her marriage being fixed up. "I am in love with you. I can't marry someone else. Please help me, O Krishna!" Rukmini wrote. A messenger carried her letter to Krishna.

When Krishna read the letter, he was charged with emotion and fell deeply in love with Rukmini. He gave a verbal reply to the messenger. "Tell Rukmini to come to the temple before her marriage rites. I will be waiting there!" said Krishna.

Rukmini was delighted at Krishna's reply. She didn't interrupt Rukmi in arranging her marriage, for it would create suspicion. On the wedding day, she was taken to the temple. Rukmi was happy that his sister had forgotten Krishna.

Soon, the prayers were finished at the temple and it was time to return to the palace for the wedding. Suddenly, two hands gently swept off Rukmini and she landed in a chariot. Standing next to her was Krishna. Rukmini blushed with joy.

Krishna whipped his horse and before anyone could understand anything, they were on their way. When Rukmi saw this, he was mad with anger. "Stop them! They should not escape!" he commanded his army. Krishna's chariot flew like the winds.

Meanwhile, Krishna's brother Balram came to know about all this. "Krishna may need my help!" he thought and came with an army, to help Krishna. A fierce battle ensued. Balram and his army soon overpowered Rukmi's army.

Rukmi was becoming desperate. He aimed at Krishna and shot an arrow. In reply, Krishna began to shower arrows on Rukmi's chariot. In no time, the wheels of Rukmi's chariot were shattered and down fell Rukmi with a loud howl.

Krishna jumped off his chariot, holding a sword, and ran towards Rukmi. He raised his sword to behead Rukmi. Just then Rukmini came running in and fell in Krishna's feet. "Please spare Rukmi. After all he is my brother!" she begged.

Taking note of Rukmini's feelings, Krishna withdrew his sword. Balram then led Krishna and Rukmini to Dwarka. There were celebrations all around. The people sang and danced in joy. Krishna married Rukmini and lived happily ever after.

Shiva and Bhasmasura

SHIVA AND BHASMASURA

Long ago, there lived a demon king named Bhasmasura. He was brave and powerful; he had health, wealth and prosperity. Still the king was often sad. The reason was that he was not at all impressive and so his subjects often ignored him.

One day, Bhasmasura decided to put an end to his sadness. "I shall pray to Lord Shiva and get his blessings," he thought, "I have heard anything can be asked from Lord Shiva when he is happy. Let me appease him." So, he began to meditate.

Bhasmasura gave up food and sleep, and sat in deep meditation, chanting the name of Lord Shiva. Days passed into months and months passed into years. Finally, Lord Shiva appeared before Bhasmasura. "I am pleased, Bhasmasura!" Shiva said.

Bhasmasura was overwhelmed to see his Lord standing before him. Without wasting any time, Bhasmasura said, "Bless me, O Lord, with such power that if I touch someone with my right hand, he may burn to ashes." "So be it!" said Shiva.

Bhasmasura thanked Shiva for the boon. But he wanted to test the effectiveness of the boon. So, he said, "Let me see, O Lord, whether the boon really works!" And so saying, Bhasmasura extended his right hand to touch Shiva. Shiva was horrified.

Now Shiva realised his blunder. "I should have thought before granting him the boon," he murmured. But now it was too late. Running to save his life, Shiva went to Lord Vishnu and said, "Please do something; save me from Bhasmasura!"

Vishnu instantly took the form of a beautiful nymph, named 'Mohini', and came in the way of Bhasmasura. "Stop there, O handsome one!" Mohini said, smiling at Bhasmasura. The demon king was enchanted by Mohini's beauty.

"Who are you, O young maiden?" asked Bhasmasura. "I am a nymph!" replied Mohini. "Will you marry me?" Bhasmasura proposed. "On one condition," Mohini said, "That you'll have to dance with me, the way I dance." Bhasmasura agreed.

Mohini danced and Bhasmasura imitated her steps. Bhasmasura was carried away in an ecstasy he had never felt before. And then suddenly, Mohini touched her head with her right hand. Imitating her, the demon king, too, touched his head.

And then what! As soon as Bhasmasura touched his head, he was set ablaze. "Oh, I had forgotten about the boon Shiva gave me," cried Bhasmasura. But it was too late. In no time, he was turned down to ashes. He was punished for being wicked.

Vishnu then transformed into his original form. Shiva heaved a huge sigh of relief. "I've learnt a lesson!" he said. "Now on, think before you grant any boon, O Lord!" said Vishnu, with a pleasant smile. Shiva thanked Vishnu and took leave of him.

Indra and his Cows

INDRA AND HIS COWS

Once, Lord Indra's cows disappeared mysteriously. "What could've happened to the cows?" Lord Indra pondered, "Did they walk away themselves? Or, someone chimed them? Or..." Getting worried, Indra called on the sages.

The sages closed their eyes and thought for a while. Then they said in unison, "The Cow's have been stolen, O Indra!" "But who stole away my cows?" Indra asked, getting anxious. "A demon tribe living across the river Rasa!" replied the sages.

"Where have the demons hidden my cows?" asked Indra. "These demons are powered with celestial magic," said the sages, "Perhaps, they have kept the cows in the dense forests across the river. But those forests are almost unaccessible."

Indra was worried. "We can't sit back!" he said, "My cows are not only a source of milk but they are also needed for rituals and ceremonies. We have to find them out!" But none of the inmates of heaven volunteered to bring back the cows.

Suddenly, Indra was reminded of something and his eyes lit up in joy. "I have someone who will surely find out my cows!" he chirped. "Who is that?" the other gods asked. "You'll know it soon!" said Indra. And he began to whistle.

Indra whistled again. And this time louder! Suddenly, the barking of a dog was heard. Everyone turned around and saw a dog coming there. It was Sarama, the She-Dog of the skies. "Woof! Woof!" she asked, "What's the matter, my lord?"

"You have always helped me out of tough situations, Sarama!" said Indra, "I am sure you will help me this time too." Then Indra told her all about the cows, how the demon tribe had stolen them and kept them in the forests across the river Rasa.

"I will bring the cows out of the dangerous forest," said Sarama, "Then it's your task to bring them back across the river." "Fine!" said Indra. "But for that you'll have to promise to supply milk to my descendants forever. Do you agree?" asked Sarama.

Sarama started off. Reaching the banks of river Rasa, she prayed for a moment, then jumped into the river and began to swim. The current of the river was hurting and Sarama was totally exhausted when she reached the other bank of the river.

Then Sarama entered into the dense forest and began to sniff. At one place, she got the smell of Indra's cows. "They must be around!" she thought. And then in a barn, she saw the cows. She secretly led the cows to the bank of the river.

Meanwhile, the demons saw Sarama and attacked her. But by then, Indra and his army had reached there. In a fierce battle, the gods defeated the demons and freed Indra's cows. As promised, Indra provided milk to Sarama's descendants forever.

Durga Slays Mahishasura

DURGA SLAYS MAHISHASURA

A demon named Mahishasura once performed severe penance and appeased Lord Brahma. "I am pleased with you!" said Brahma, "Ask what you may!" Mahishasura said, "Let my death be not caused by any man or God."

Mahishasura was now invincible. He began to harass the people. Soon, he turned towards the heaven. Now, the gods got scared and ran to Lord Brahma. "It's all my fault," Brahma repented, "I shouldn't have given him the boon."

So, they all went to the abode of Shiva.
"Mahishasura can't be killed by a man
or a god!" said Brahma. "Then let us all
combine our powers and evoke a woman,
who would be able to kill Mahishasura,"
Shiva proposed. All the gods agreed.

So, all of them sat together and began to meditate. As their celestial powers combined, there formed a halo around. And out came a powerful beam of light. It took the form of a woman, having a thousand arms. She was called 'Durga'.

All the gods then prayed to Durga,
"O Goddess! You are the source of all
strength. Destroy Mahishasura and
protect us." Shiva drew a trident and
offered it to Durga. Vishnu and other
gods, too, gave their weapons to Durga.

Thus armed with the celestial weapons, Durga mounted on a lion and set out in search of Mahishasura. She looked fierce as death. As Durga descended to earth, the mountains shook and the seas trembled. The goddess seethed in anger.

Mahishasura heard the mighty roar of the lion and rushed out of his palace to find out the matter. When he saw Durga, suddenly he broke into a laughter. "Oh, a woman mounting on a lion. Ha! Ha! Am I scared?" Durga looked at the demon.

"Behold, Mahishasura!" Durga shouted at him. "I am your death!" "Death? Hah! A mere woman!" Mahishasura mocked at the goddess. "I am no mere woman. I've come to fulfill Brahma's boon!" said Durga. Mahishasura was puzzled.

"You wished that no man or god would kill
you, right?" asked Durga. "Yes, I did!"
said the demon, "And that means I am
invincible! Ha! Ha! Ha!" "No more!" cried
the goddess. "I have come to kill you!
A man can not but a woman can kill you!"

Mahishasura was alarmed. He assumed the form of a buffalo and charged at Durga. Suddenly, Durga's lion roared and attacked the buffalo. Now, the buffalo took the form of a lion. Durga flung her trident and hacked off the lion's head.

But the lion was just an illusion. From
its body emerged the buffalo-demon
again. This time Durga didn't give him
any chance. She hacked off his head.
Thus, the goddess killed Mahishasura.
The heaven and earth breathed a sigh
of relief.

Rantideva and the Gods

RANTIDEVA AND THE GODS

One day, Lord Brahma thought, "Lord Vishnu claims to have many devotees. Let me find out who is his greatest devotee!" So thinking, Brahma called on the other gods and together they went to 'Baikuntha', Lord Vishnu's abode.

Vishnu welcomed them and asked the reason for their visit. Brahma said, "Lord, we all know you have many devotees. But whom do you think is your greatest devotee?" "Rantideva!" Vishnu replied without any hitch and pause.

Brahma was surprised at Vishnu's reply.
Rantideva was a king, living on earth. He
was Vishnu's ardent devotee. He had
given up his kingdom and had been
fasting for forty-eight days. "What is so
special about Rantideva?" Brahma asked.

"Today is the last day of Rantideva's fasting. He will be breaking his fast anytime. Please allow us to test him, O Lord!" said Indra. "Sure! Just test him and you'll find out why I consider him a great devotee," Vishnu said with a smile.

So, Brahma, Indra and the other gods descended to earth. Meanwhile, Rantideva was about to break his fast. He closed his eyes and prayed to Lord Vishnu, "May you be pleased, O Lord! I am breaking my fast and taking this food in your name."

Just as Rantideva was about to take his first bite, there came a Brahmin. He called out to Rantideva, "O holy one! I am very hungry. Please give me some food!" "Here, take half of this!" said Rantideva and gave half of his food to the Brahmin.

Next came a poor farmer asking for food. Rantideva gave him some of his food. "His hunger is greater than mine. I am lucky I could offer him something!" he thought. Then came a beggar. And Rantideva gave him whatever food he was left with.

Actually, the Brahmin, the farmer and the beggar were the gods. They were surprised at Rantideva's kind-heartedness. "How could he part with his food so easily? He was himself so hungry!" wondered Indra. "Let's take a last test!" said Brahma.

Brahma asked Yama, the God of Death, to test Rantideva. Meanwhile, Rantideva thought, "I shall drink some water and break my fast!" Yama, disguised as an untouchable, went moaning to Rantideva, "Water... water! I am very thirsty!"

"Here, take this!" said Rantideva. "But I am an untouchable. I can't touch your pot," said Yama. "No one is untouchable, brother!" said Rantideva, "Lord Vishnu resides in all of us!" "But won't your penance be incomplete?" asked Yama.

The gods were pleased. Rantideva had proved himself to be selfless and virtuous. Vishnu and all the gods appeared before him and blessed him. "You see me in all the creatures, Rantideva!" Vishnu said, "You are indeed my greatest devotee."

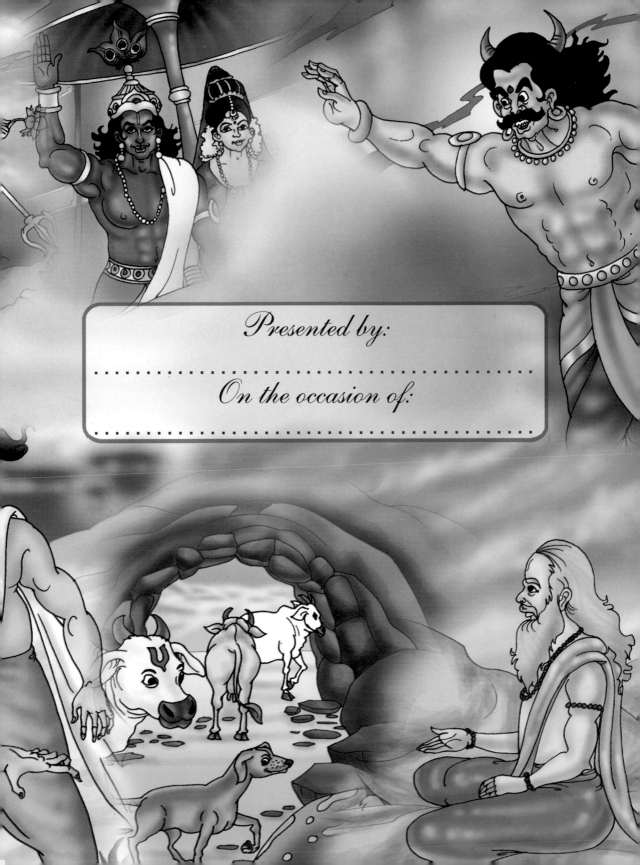

Presented by:

. . . .

On the occasion of:

. . . .